RICHARD WAGNER

TRISTAN UND ISOLDE

Vorspiel und Isoldes Liebestod
Prelude and Liebestod
WWV 90

Edited by/Herausgegeben von
Egon Voss

T0080315

Ernst Eulenburg Ltd

London · Mainz · Madrid · New York · Paris · Prague · Tokyo · Toronto · Zürich

CONTENTS

Reprinted from *Richard Wagner: Sämtliche Werke*
Volume 8/I and 8/III by permission of Schott Music GmbH & Co. KG

Ernst Eulenburg Ltd
48 Great Marlborough Street
London W1F 7BB

PREFACE

The Tristan material was first of topical interest to Wagner in autumn 1854, though the work – as far as can be gathered from Wagner's few statements of that time – at first looked entirely different from what would later be executed.[1] Wagner wanted 'to leave a memorial' to love as the 'most beautiful of all dreams', as he wrote Franz Liszt in December 1854.[2] It is not known when the concept changed. In any case, in August 1856 Wagner suddenly described the subject of the work as 'love as a terrible anguish',[3] and he then also implemented it accordingly. The first dated sketch stemmed from December 1856. At the same time typically enough it was not a sketch of the text, but a music sketch,[4] concurring with Wagner's oft-quoted later statement that with *Tristan* he had had the urge 'to break out musically as if I were writing a symphony' (28 September 1878).[5] This aspect also plays a part in the 'programmatic commentary' given below for the Prelude.

Wagner began steady work on the piece in August 1857. He proceeded as usual: the libretto was written from a draft of the text in prose, followed by the composing which was carried out in three steps. The compositional sketch (first complete draft), the comparatively more extensive orchestral sketch (second complete draft) and the score were written in parallel, but naturally moved along chronologically one after the other. This was finished by 6 August 1859. It was, in fact, printed immediately, yet the work came to first performance only on 10 June 1865 in Munich. The performance rehabilitated the work that had previously been considered unplayable after an unsuccessful, incomplete rehearsal period in Vienna of several years. *Tristan* had made its way, though only slowly.

Hans von Bülow (1830–1894), conductor of the premiere, was also the first to perform the Prelude for the first time separately, and indeed in a concert on 12 March 1859 in Prague. On this occasion Bülow produced a concert ending,[6] since Wagner himself had refused to furnish such. Bülow's ending did not however appeal to Wagner; this now led to his composing a concert ending of his own for his Parisian concerts in 1860, in which he himself wanted to conduct the Prelude. It is included in the present edition preceding the stage ending. Wagner characteristically did not leave it at that, but along with the Prelude in the new form still sent a verbal commentary for the audience, a 'Programmatic Commentary', as he called it. It reads:[7]

Prelude to Tristan and Isolde.

An ancient and original love poem, inexhaustibly varied anew in all languages of medieval Europe, tells us of Tristan and Isolde. The loyal vassal had wooed Isolde for his king, without daring to confess his own love for her who followed him as the betrothed of his Master, because she helplessly had to follow the wooer himself. The Goddess of Love, jealous of her suppressed rights, took revenge: through an ingenious oversight she let the love potion – intended by the cautious mother for the couple betrothed only because of politics, as was the custom of the times – be proffered to the youthful pair, that by its consumption their love, suddenly blazing up in bright flames, made them avow that they belong only to each other. Now there was to be no end to the longing, desiring, the bliss and the misery of love: world, power, fame, praise, radiance, honour, chivalry,

[1] Egon Voss, 'Die "schwarze und die weiße Flagge". Zur Entstehung von Wagners "Tristan"', in: *Archiv für Musikwissenschaft* LIV, Vol. 3 (1997), 210–227
[2] Richard Wagner, *Sämtliche Briefe*, Vol. VI, eds. Hans-Joachim Bauer and Johannes Forner, (Leipzig, 1986), 299
[3] Richard Wagner, *Sämtliche Briefe*, Vol. VIII, eds. Hans-Joachim Bauer and Johannes Forner, (Leipzig, 1991), 156
[4] Facsimile and Transcription in: Voss (see note 1), 222f
[5] Cosima Wagner, *Die Tagebücher*, eds. Martin Gregor-Dellin and Dietrich Mack, Vol. II (Munich/Zurich, 1977), 185
[6] Richard Wagner, *Sämtliche Werke*, Vol. 27, *Documents and Texts for 'Tristan und Isolde'*, eds. Gabriele E. Meyer and Egon Voss (Mainz, 2008), 66f (Document No. 155)
[7] ibid., 93f. (Document No. 238)

loyalty, friendship, all scattered like an insubstantial dream; only one thing was left alive: longing, longing insatiable, ever renewed yearning, – starved and parched; only one deliverance – death, dying, perishing, nevermore to awaken!

As the musician who chose this subject for the introduction of his drama of love here felt himself entirely within the most characteristic, unrestricted elements of music, he need only be concerned about how to stay within limits, since exhausting the subject is impossible. Thus, he then let the insatiable yearning swell but once, though in broadly-structured stages, from the shy confession of the slightest attraction, through anxious sighing, hoping and fearing, lamenting and wishing, delighting and tormenting, up to the most powerful onrush, to the most forcible effort to find the breach, to disclose to the heart the way into the sea of love's unending bliss. To no avail! Impotently the heart sinks back, languishing in longing, in longing without attaining, since every attaining can only engender new longing, until in the final exhaustion of the refracted glance the presentiment of highest blissful attainment dawns: it is the rapture of dying, of nonbeing henceforth, the final release into that wonderful realm from which we stray the furthest when we with most passionate force strive to force an entry into it. Do we call it death? Or is it the nocturnal wonder world from which, as legend tells us, ivy and vine sprang up in ardent embrace on Tristan's and Isolde's grave?

In this form Wagner performed the Prelude not only several times in Paris, but also in his concert on 8 February 1863 in Prague. But after that he decided in favour of another form, namely, the one used today. In it the stage ending, thus to bar 111 (p17), is joined without transition to the end of the opera, Act III, bb1621–1699. In the process the ending remains instrumentally intact, although the vocal part is dropped. The Prelude was first heard in this form on 26 February 1863 in St Petersburg under Wagner's di-

rection, and time and again the composer drew up a 'Programmatic Commentary' for it:[8]

Tristan and Isolde / Prelude and Transfiguration.
A.) Prelude. (Love Death.)
Tristan, as suitor, brings Isolde to his king and uncle. The two are in love. From the most bashful lament of unquenchable yearning, from gentlest shudder to terrible outbreak, confessing hopeless love, the feeling advances through all phases of the unsuccessful struggle against inner ardour until powerless, it sinks back into itself, seeming to depart into death.
B.) Final Section. (Transfiguration.)
Yet, what Fate parted for life now revives transfigured in death: the gateway of union is opened. Over Tristan's body the dying Isolde becomes aware of the most blessed fulfilment of ardent longing: eternal union in immeasurable space, without limit, without restraint, inseparable!–

It is above all noteworthy that Wagner applied to the Prelude the title 'Liebestod' [Love Death], which is the usual title today for the ending, and characterized the ending as 'Transfiguration'. The Prelude was performed in this version nearly 20 times between 1863 and 1877. Nonetheless, his usage, behind which obviously stood a firm understanding of the matter, did not succeed. Even his contemporaries already called the conclusion 'Liebestod'.

The music text follows the *Richard Wagner Edition, Collected Works*, Vol. 8, I–III, Tristan und Isolde WWV 90, eds. Isolde Vetter and Egon Voss (Mainz, 1990–1993). The accompanying critical report is located in Vol. 8, III, 210–227. For further information, cf. *Richard Wagner, Collected Works*, Vol. 27, *Documents and Texts for 'Tristan und Isolde'*, eds. Gabriele E. Meyer and Egon Voss (Mainz, 2008).

Egon Voss
Translation: Margit McCorkle

8 ibid., 145 (Document No. 419)

VORWORT

Der Tristan-Stoff wurde für Wagner erstmals im Herbst 1854 aktuell, doch sah das Werk – soweit sich das aus Wagners wenigen Äußerungen aus jener Zeit erschließen lässt – zunächst ganz anders aus, als es dann ausgeführt wurde.[1] Wagner wollte der Liebe als dem „schönsten aller Träume" ein „Denkmal setzen", wie er im Dezember 1854 an Franz Liszt schrieb.[2] Wann sich das Konzept änderte, ist unbekannt. Jedenfalls bezeichnete Wagner im August 1856 plötzlich „die Liebe als furchtbare Qual" als Thema des Werks[3], und dementsprechend führte er es dann auch aus. Die erste datierte Aufzeichnung stammt vom Dezember 1856. Dabei handelt es sich bezeichnenderweise nicht um eine Text-, sondern um eine Notenskizze[4], was mit Wagners oft zitierter späterer Äußerung übereinstimmt, er habe beim *Tristan* das Bedürfnis gehabt, „sich musikalisch auszurasen, wie wenn ich eine Symphonie geschrieben hätte" (28. September 1878).[5] Dieser Aspekt spielt auch in der unten wiedergegebenen „Programmatischen Erläuterung" zum Vorspiel eine Rolle.

Mit der kontinuierlichen Arbeit am Werk begann Wagner im August 1857. Er verfuhr wie gewohnt: Nach einem Textentwurf in Prosa entstand das Textbuch, daran schloss sich die Komposition an, die sich in drei Schritten vollzog. Parallel, aber natürlich zeitlich gegeneinander versetzt, wurden die Kompositionsskizze (Erster Gesamtentwurf), die demgegenüber ausführlichere Orchesterskizze (Zweiter Gesamtentwurf) und die Partitur geschrieben. Diese lag am 6. August 1859 fertig vor. Sie wurde zwar sogleich gedruckt, doch zur ersten Aufführung kam das Werk erst am 10. Juni 1865 in München. Sie rehabilitierte das Werk, das zuvor nach mehrjähriger, erfolglos abgebrochener Probenzeit in Wien als unspielbar gegolten hatte. Durchgesetzt hat sich der *Tristan* allerdings nur langsam.

Hans von Bülow (1830–1894), der Dirigent der Uraufführung, war auch der erste, der das Vorspiel erstmals separat aufführte, und zwar in einem Konzert am 12. März 1859 in Prag. Bülow stellte aus diesem Anlass einen Konzertschluss her[6], da Wagner sich geweigert hatte, einen solchen einzurichten. Bülows Schluss fand Wagners Gefallen jedoch nicht, was dazu führte, dass Wagner für seine Pariser Konzerte 1860, in denen er selbst das Vorspiel dirigieren wollte, nun doch selbst einen Konzertschluss komponierte. Er wird in der vorliegenden Ausgabe – vor dem Bühnenschluss – mitgeteilt. Charakteristisch für Wagner ist, dass er es dabei nicht beließ, sondern dem Vorspiel in der neuen Gestalt noch einen verbalen Kommentar für das Publikum mitgab, eine „Programmatische Erläuterung", wie er es nannte. Sie lautet[7]:

Vorspiel zu Tristan u. Isolde.

Ein altes, unerlöschlich neu sich gestaltendes, in allen Sprachen des mittelalterlichen Europas nachgedichtetes, Ur-Liebesgedicht sagt uns von Tristan und Isolde. Der treue Vasall hatte für seinen König diejenige gefreit, die selbst zu lieben er sich nicht gestehen wollte, Isolden, die ihm als Braut seines Herren folgte, weil sie dem Freier selbst machtlos folgen musste. Die auf ihre unterdrückten Rechte eifersüchtige Liebesgöttin rächte sich: den, der Zeitsitte gemäss für den nur durch Politik vermählten Gatten durch die vorsorgliche Mutter bestimmten Liebestrank, lässt sie durch ein erfindungsreiches Versehen dem jugendlichen Paare credenzen das, durch seinen Genuss plötzlich in hellen Flammen

---

[1] Egon Voss, „Die ‚schwarze und die weiße Flagge'. Zur Entstehung von Wagners ‚Tristan'" in: *Archiv für Musikwissenschaft* LIV, Heft 3 (1997), S. 210–227.

[2] Richard Wagner, *Sämtliche Briefe*, Bd. VI, hg. v. Hans-Joachim Bauer und Johannes Forner, Leipzig 1986, S. 299.

[3] Richard Wagner, *Sämtliche Briefe*, Bd. VIII, hg. v. Hans-Joachim Bauer und Johannes Forner, Leipzig 1991, S. 156.

[4] Faksimile und Übertragung in: Voss (wie Anmerkung 1), S. 222f.

[5] Cosima Wagner, *Die Tagebücher*, hg. v. Martin Gregor-Dellin und Dietrich Mack, Bd. II, München/Zürich 1977, S. 185.

[6] Richard Wagner, *Sämtliche Werke* Bd. 27, *Dokumente und Texte zu „Tristan und Isolde"*, hg. v. Gabriele E. Meyer und Egon Voss, Mainz 2008, S. 66f (Dokument Nr. 155).

[7] Ebda., S. 93f. (Dokument Nr. 238).

auflodernd, sich gestehen muss, dass nur sie einander gehören. Nun war des Sehnens, des Verlangens, der Wonnen und des Elendes der Liebe kein Ende: Welt, Macht, Ruhm, Glanz, Ehre, Ritterlichkeit, Treue, Freundschaft, alles wie wesenloser Traum zerstoben; nur Eines noch lebend: Sehnsucht, Sehnsucht, unstillbares, ewig neu sich gebärendes Verlangen, – Schmachten und Dürsten; einzige Erlösung – Tod, Sterben, Untergehen, Nichtmehrerwachen!

Der Musiker, der dieses Thema sich für die Einleitung seines Liebesdramas wählte, konnte, da er hier ganz im eigensten, unbeschränkten Elemente der Musik sich fühlte, nur dafür besorgt sein, wie er sich beschränkte, da Erschöpfung des Themas unmöglich ist. So liess er denn nur einmal, aber im lang gegliederten Zuge, das unersättliche Verlangen anschwellen, von dem schüchternden Bekenntniss, der zartesten Hingezogenheit an, durch zagendes Seufzen, Hoffen und Bangen, Klagen und Wünschen, Wonnen und Qualen, bis zum mächtigsten Andrang, zur gewaltsamsten Mühe, den Durchbruch zu finden, der dem Herzen den Weg in das Meer unendlicher Liebeswonne eröffne. Umsonst! Ohnmächtig sinkt das Herz zurück, in Sehnsucht zu verschmachten, in Sehnsucht ohne Erreichen, da jedes Erreichen nur neues Sehnen keimen lässt, bis im letzten Ermatten dem brechenden Blicke die Ahnung höchster Wonne des Erlangens aufdämmert: es ist die Wonne des Sterbens, des Nichtmehrseins, der letzten Erlösung in jenes wundervolle Reich, von dem wir am fernsten abirren, wenn wir mit stürmischster Gewalt darin einzudringen uns mühen. Nennen wir es Tod? Oder ist es die nächtige Wunderwelt, aus der ein Epheu und eine Rebe zu inniger Umschlingung auf Tristans und Isoldes Grabe emporwuchsen, wie die Sage uns meldet?

In dieser Form führte Wagner das Vorspiel nicht nur mehrfach in Paris auf, sondern auch in seinem Konzert am 8. Februar 1863 in Prag. Danach aber entschied er sich für eine andere Form, nämlich die heute allgemein gebräuchliche. In ihr wird an den Bühnenschluss, also an Takt 111 (S. 17), der Schluss der Oper, 3. Aufzug Takt 1621–1699, übergangslos angeschlossen. Dabei bleibt der Schluss instrumentatorisch unangetastet, obwohl die Singstimme entfällt. In

dieser Gestalt erklang das Vorspiel erstmals am 26. Februar 1863 in St. Petersburg unter Wagners Leitung, und abermals verfasste der Komponist eine „Programmatische Erläuterung" dazu[8]:

Tristan und Isolde / Vorspiel und Schlusssatz.
A.) Vorspiel. (Liebestod.)
Tristan führt, als Brautwerber, Isolde seinem Könige und Oheim zu. Beide lieben sich. Von der schüchternsten Klage des unstillbaren Verlangens, vom zartesten Erbeben bis zum furchtbaren Ausbruch des Bekenntnisses hoffnungsloser Liebe, durchschreitet die Empfindung alle Phasen des sieglosen Kampfes gegen die innere Glut, bis sie, ohnmächtig in sich zurücksinkend, wie im Tode zu verlöschen scheint.
B.) Schlusssatz. (Verklärung.)
Doch, was das Schicksal für das Leben trennte, lebt nun verklärt im Tode auf: die Pforte der Vereinigung ist geöffnet. Über Tristans Leiche gewahrt die sterbende Isolde die seligste Erfüllung des glühenden Sehnens: ewige Vereinigung in ungemessenen Räumen, ohne Schranken, ohne Banden, unzertrennbar! –

Bemerkenswert ist vor allem, dass Wagner den heute für den Schluss gebräuchlichen Titel „Liebestod" auf das Vorspiel bezog und den Schluss als „Verklärung" kennzeichnete. Fast zwanzigmal führte er zwischen 1863 und 1877 das Vorspiel in dieser Version auf. Dennoch hat sich sein Sprachgebrauch, hinter dem selbstverständlich ein dezidiertes Verständnis der Sache steht, nicht durchgesetzt. Auch die Zeitgenossen bezeichneten den Schluss schon als „Liebestod".

Der Notentext folgt der Ausgabe *Richard Wagner, Sämtliche Werke* Bd. 8, I–III, *Tristan und Isolde* WWV 90 hg. v. Isolde Vetter und Egon Voss, Mainz 1990–1993. Der zugehörige Kritische Bericht findet sich in Bd. 8, III, S. 210–227. Für weitere Informationen vgl. *Richard Wagner, Sämtliche Werke* Bd. 27, *Dokumente und Texte zu „Tristan und Isolde"*, hg. v. Gabriele E. Meyer und Egon Voss, Mainz 2008.

Egon Voss

---

[8] Ebda., S. 145 (Dokument Nr. 419).

TRISTAN UND ISOLDE
Einleitung

Richard Wagner
(1813–1883)

Edited by Egon Voss
© 2011 Ernst Eulenburg Ltd, London/Mainz

4

5

11

Konzertschluß

Bühnenschluß

TRISTAN UND ISOLDE

Liebestod

Richard Wagner
(1813–1883)
WWV 90

ISOLDE: Mild und lei- se wie er lä- chelt, wie das Au - ge hold er öff - net, — seht ihr's, Freun-de?

Edited by Egon Voss
© 2011 Ernst Eulenburg Ltd, London/Mainz

T. 1626-1654 Kb: Die Anweisung „nur die l. Hälfte" in T. 1654 scheint zu implizieren, daß zuvor mehr als die Hälfte bzw. alle Kb gespielt haben. Die Quellen enthalten jedoch zwischen T. 1626 und 1654 keinen Hinweis auf einen Wiedereintritt aller Kb. („Zusammen", wie es in T. 1627 steht, bedeutet in Wagners Ge-brauch nur das Zusammenspiel zuvor geteilter Gruppen,hier also der in T. 1623 verlangten 4 Kb.)

Bars 1626-1654 Kb: the instruction 'nur die l. Hälfte' [=first half only] at bar 1654 appears to imply that previously more than half double basses, or indeed all of them, have been playing. The sources do not however show any indication of re-entry of all the double basses between bars 1626 and 1654. (The instruc-struction 'Zusammen' [together] at bar 1627, signifies, as used by Wagner, merely that groups which were previously divided are now to play together, i.e. in this case the four double basses required at bar 1623).

ISOLDE: Lüf - te? Sind es Wol - ken won - ni-ger Düf - - te? Wie sie schwel - - len, mich um-

ISOLDE: -rau - - schen, soll ich at - - men, soll ich lau - - schen? Soll ich schlür-fen, un-ter-tau - chen?

32

36